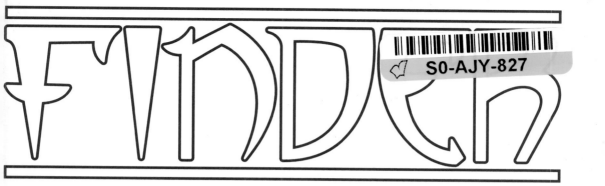

FINDER

"No matter
how **HOT**
you are,

No matter
how **RICH**,
how **SMART**,
how **COOL**
you are,

LIGHTSPEED PRESS

"somebody,

somewhere

LOGISTICS **MIKE MCNEIL**

PRODUCTION **VINCENT SNEED** ACOUSTICS **SHAUN CAPUT**

FIVE CRAZY WOMEN

"*is* SICK *of your* SHIT."

DEDICATION

HE KNOWS WHO
HE KNOWS WHY

CHAPTER ONE:

BEWARE
OF
DOG

YOU AIN' NOTHIN'
BUT A HOUN' DOG-AH,
HANGIN' ROUND
MY DOOR--

YOU AIN' NOTHIN'
BUT A HOUN' DOG-AH,
HANGIN' ROUND
MY DOOR--

WELL, YOU CAN
WAG YOUR TAIL, BUT--
I AIN'T GONNA FEED
YOU NO MORE--

NIT
NIT
DOOP
DIT
DOOT

BROOOP.

BROOOP.

≶CLICK≶

HI, THIS IS VANYA. I'M
NOT AWAKE RIGHT NOW. DON'T
LEAVE A MESSAGE, I NEVER
LISTEN TO THEM. ≶BEEEP≶

6

=AHEM= OOKA OOOKA OOOGH OOOGHA OOGH AH-AH-AH **AAAAH!**

=BEEEP=

=COUGH=

ANY
BE
BOOP
BIP
BE

HI. THIS IS SHERRY. THIS IS NOT-- I REPEAT-- **NOT** MIRIAM. SHE DOES **NOT** LIVE HERE. I GOT HER NUMBER BY ACCIDENT.

SHE IS A TOTAL COW AND I WILL NOT PASS MESSAGES. IF YOU ARE ONE OF HER LAME-ASS FRIENDS, I AM **NOT** INTERESTED IN **YOU**. MOM, YOU CAN REACH ME ON MY HAND-PHONE. MIRIAM, CHOKE BLOOD AND DIE.

=BEEEP=

HI, SHERRY. I DON'T CARE ABOUT MIRIAM. SHE'S NUTS AND **YOU** SOUND FAR MORE INTERESTING. I ASSURE YOU, IT WILL DRIVE MIRIAM **RIGHT** INTO THERAPY IF SHE SEES YOU WITH ME.

UNFORTUNATELY, YOU CAN'T CALL ME, 'CAUSE I DON'T HAVE A PHONE. SO UNTIL I'M LUCKY ENOUGH TO RECOGNIZE YOUR VOICE DRIFTING ACROSS THE MARBLE COURTS OF BALAIT, WE'LL JUST HAVE OUR IMAGINATIONS TO KEEP US AMUSED. MY NAME IS JAEGER. BYE NOW.

DOOT
DYEET
NIT
DOOP
DIP

=BREEP=

=BREEP=

BEEP

HELLO?

MATTIE! HOW YA BEEN?

MM? I'M GOOD--

GOOD. GOOD-- LISTEN, I'M BACK IN TOWN. I WAS OUT IN THE SOUTH WOODS, BUT I GOT AN ITCH TO SEE YOU. WANT SOME DINNER?

IT'S MIDNIGHT SNACK FOR **ME.** I'M ALMOST TOTALLY NOCTURNAL THESE DAYS--

COOL, ME TOO--

SINCE I MET LEANDRA, I SWITCHED TO THIRD SHIFT, AND I'M REALLY LIKING IT. Y'KNOW?

YEAH, OKAY.

I'D STILL LIKE TO **SEE** YOU, THOUGH.

NO BIG THING, BABY. I HOPE YOU'RE VERY HAPPY.

OH, I **AM.** AND I'M WORKING ON LOOSENING HER UP.

MAYBE **NEXT** TIME YOU'LL GET A **REAL** WELCOME HOME.

DULY NOTED, GORGEOUS. SORRY TO WAKE YOU.

BYE, BABY.

MM!

DON'T HELP ME MUCH **NOW,** THOUGH...

DYIP EET EET EET DEET DOOP

GOOD EVENING, SIMONE CÉZARE.

GOOD EVENING TO **YOU,** MADE-MOISELLE.

JAEGER! OH **HELLO,** HONEY! WHEN DID **YOU** GET BACK INTO TOWN??

JUST NOW. I TELL YA, I GOT DUST IN CREASES I NEVER KNEW I **HAD.** I NEED PROFESSIONAL HELP. YOU'RE MY ANGEL OF PINK SOAP AND FLOOFY TOWELS. WHATTAYA SAY?

HELL AND DAMMIT IS WHAT I SAY. I HAVE CLIENTS STACKED UP LIKE FIREWOOD. THIS IS MY BUSY TIME-- PEOPLE GET DEPRESSED AFTER CARNIVAL.

PWOOF

CAN YOU WAIT A MONTH? I CAN'T **STAND** TO LEAVE **YOU** WITH A QUICK SCRUB AND A HAND-JOB.

8

=SIGH= WELL, I CAN'T SAY IT AIN'T WORTH THE WAIT. IN A MONTH, THEN.

SORRY, SUGAR. GO PROWL. **YOU** WON'T BE LONELY FOR LONG.

MAAAN...!

DEET DEET DIT DEET DOOP DIT!

HEEEY, JANNIE. WHAT'S FOR DINNER?

JAEGER??

OH YEAH-- YOU VANISH FOR EIGHT MONTHS AND NOW YOU EXPECT ME TO **COOK** FOR YOU?

COURSE NOT, J; I'LL DO THE COOKIN'.

...SO... YOU'RE... INVITING ME TO **YOUR** PLACE?

HEY, IT'S *ME*-- I DON'T HAVE A PLACE.

THEN **WHERE** ARE YOU COOKING DINNER?

YOUR PLACE. NATCH.

SO WHAT'S FOR DINNER?

I DUNNO; WHATCHA GOT?

OH FOR CRYIN' OUT LOUD-- YOU **REALLY** TAKE THE CAKE, DON'T YOU?

CAKE? OH **HELL** YEAH, I MAKE GREAT CAKE. YOU GOT BLUE-BERRIES? NEVER MIND IF YOU DON'T, I KNOW WHERE--

LOOK, I'M *MARRIED!* I MARRIED JACK OPALANA--

DAMN, TOWNIE WOMEN ARE WEIRD!

THE *LAST* TIME I WAS IN THIS PART OF TOWN, THEY WERE BENDING GOLF CLUBS OVER EACH OTHER'S HEADS TO GET TO ME!

NOW I'M LIKE A LEPER IN A PUBLIC BATH! BEEN A FIRE SALE ON *VIBRATORS* AROUND HERE?

≡SNERKK≡

≡HEH-HEH-HEH≡ JAEGER, YOU *KILL* ME. ≡HEH-HEH-HEH≡

WHAAT? HELL, I CAN SLEEP ANYWHERE--

-- IF I WANTED TO SLEEP IN A *TREE* I COULDA STAYED *OUTSIDE* WHERE IT DON'T *STINK* SO BAD.

ALL I WANT'S SOME CLEAN SHEETS AND HOT WATER. I'LL STAY OUT OF THEIR HAIR--

YOU NEED A PLACE TO *STAY*, MAN, JUST ASK--

NOOO, NO. THANKS, **NO** THANKS. NOTHING PERSONAL, I APPRECIATE IT, BUT IT'S NOT WHAT I CAME IN FOR.

I JUST WANNA KNOW WHY I'M SUDDENLY A PIECE A' SHIT-

YOU HAVE SEX WITH *STRINGS* OF WOMEN JUST TO HAVE A PLACE TO *SLEEP*, YOU DISAPPEAR IN THE *MORNING*, YOU'RE LIKE A *CAT* WITH TEN DIFFERENT FAMILIES, AND YOU *WONDER*--

I'M USED TO ASCIAN WOMEN. SHIT, *YOU'RE* WITH A DIFFERENT *GUY* EVERY NIGHT, WHAT DO *YOU* DO IN THE MORNING?

MOST GUYS DON'T STAY THAT LONG. IT'S DIFFERENT. NOT TO BEAT A DEAD HORSE--

OH, GO ON, IT'S NOT QUITE PULVERIZED YET--

YEAH, OKAY.

BUT MOST PEOPLE *I* KNOW -- MEN AND WOMEN ALIKE-- ARE SORT OF SERIALLY BISEXUAL.

BREAK UP WITH A BOYFRIEND, GET A GIRLFRIEND. DIVORCE A WIFE, TAKE UP WITH A BOY TOY. IF YOU'VE RUN OFF ALL THE WOMEN, GOD KNOWS THERE ARE MILES OF *MEN* WHO'D TAKE CARE A' THAT. HELL, THEY'D START A *CONGA* LINE.

IF YOU WEREN'T SO RELENTLESSLY STRAIGHT--

IT'S A THOUGHT... IT CLEARS THE PALATE.

TASTE, PALATE... ECH. THAT'S ALL YOU CAN EVER TALK ABOUT.

WELL, SWITCH-HITTIN' GETS YA LAID. DON'T BITCH TO *ME* IF YOU WON'T TRY THE REST OF THE MENU.

MENU! MY ASS!

WHEN'S THE LAST TIME *YOU* SAMPLED THE SEAFOOD??

YEAH, WHATEVER...

...SO... IF WHAT YOU WANT'S SOME LAY-TIME... HELL, WHY DON'T YOU GO TO A SEX CLUB?

NO, MAN...

WHY NOT? YOU USED TO BOUNCE FOR SOME SWANKY ONES. REALLY EXCLUSIVE. I **KNOW** YOU'VE GOT FRIENDS -- CAN'T ONE OF **THEM** GET YOU A MEMBERSHIP?

CAN'T PASS THE BLOOD TESTS.

SHIT, MAN, WHAT HAVE YOU **GOT?**

NOT WHAT **YOU'VE** GOT.

HUYY-YAH.

MMF. BACK.

BACK WHA?

INNA MINNIT.

UNH.

WOW. A THOUSAND-MARK.

I AIN' EVER SHEEN ONE UP CLOSE. THASS VER' INNERESHTING.

Y'DON' WANNA WAVE A THIN' LIKE THISS AROUN' HERE, MAN... PEOPLE MIGHT...

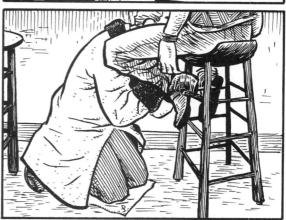

I GUESS THAT'S TRUE.

I DO A LOT OF STUFF THAT, BY CITY STANDARDS, MAKES ME LOOK LIKE AN ASSHOLE.

BULLSHIT. PARDON **ME**, BUDDY, BUT **BULLSHIT.**

YOU KNOW THE RULES, AND YOU DON'T PLAY BY THEM. YOU'RE NOT AN ASSHOLE "BY CITY STANDARDS". YOU'RE AN **ASSHOLE**, PURE AND SIMPLE.

WHY DO YOU COME TO TOWN TO GET LAID, ANYWAY? WHYDONCHA FIND AN ASCIAN CAMP, BE WITH WOMEN WHO'D **UNDERSTAND** YOU?

I'M TABOO TO THEM. I'M A SIN-EATER.

WHICH IS WHAT, EXACTLY? I WATCH THE ANTHROPOLOGY CHANNEL WITH ALL THE REST OF THE DOPES, BUT--

RITUAL PURIFIER. ITINERANT SCAPEGOAT...EH. NEAR AS **I** CAN TELL, IT'S A WAY TO CRAP ON THE LOWEST-STATUS ASCIANS. PEOPLE NOBODY'S IN A HURRY TO ADOPT. NO ORPHANS IN THE HALT... THEY WON'T TAKE YOU IN AND THEY WON'T LET YOU GO... SIN-EATER'S SUPPOSED TO BE UNTOUCHABLE.

HUH!

RIGHT.

I GET THREE KINDS OF ASCIAN WOMEN: DISGRUNTLED WIVES, DADDY'S LITTLE PRINCESSES, AND DEATH-OBSESSED PSYCHOS, ALL OF WHICH ARE ACTUALLY **ONE** KIND: PISSED-OFF WOMEN WHO WANT TO GET **BACK** AT SOMEBODY.

WHICH IS FINE IF I'M LEAVING CAMP ANYWAY...

SO I DID A HELL OF A LOT OF STUFF WITH THEM THAT *THEY* THOUGHT WAS JUST *GHASTLY* DIRTY, AND WOULD NEVER DO WITH A POTENTIAL HUSBAND... I WAS A DUMB HORNY TEENAGER, *I* THOUGHT IT WAS A GOOD DEAL.

THIS ONE GIRL, SHE WAS CRAZY ON A *STICK*. I SHOULDA KNOWN IT THE FIRST DAY I MET HER; SHE DUMPED SOURED-OUT LIQUOR MASH DOWN MY NECK AND THEN JUMPED ON ME...

FIRST FOUR OR FIVE TIMES, THOUGH, IT WAS *GREAT*-- SHE WAS *NICE* AND LIMBER--

THEN SHE STARTS IN, WANTING TO DO IT WHEN SHE'S ON HER MOON TIME- BIG NO-NO ASIDE FROM BEING *GROSS AS HELL*--

--*THEN* SHE WANTS TO, Y'KNOW, KILL A *LIZARD* OR SOMETHING BEFOREHAND AND USE *THE BLOOD*-- TELLS ME IT'S THIS SUPER SECRET WOMEN'S RITUAL, WHICH IS BULLSHIT, SHE'S MAKING IT ALL UP, BUT WHAT DO *I* KNOW?

I'M GETTING MORE AND MORE FREAKED OUT, BUT I COULDN'T SAY *NO*, SO I GOT ROUGHER AND ROUGHER, THINKING SHE'D GET FED UP AND LEAVE-- I FIGURED A BOUT OF RODEO SEX WOULD PUSH HER OVER THE EDGE FOR SURE--

"RODEO SEX"?

UH, YEAH... I'D DO HER FROM BEHIND, THEN WHEN SHE WAS *INTO* IT I'D CALL 'ER A FAT NASTY HAG CHILD OR SOME SHIT, THEN, LIKE, *HANG ON*--

≡SNICCKK≡

OH, THAT SHIT WASN'T *FUNNY*, MAN! IT PUSHED HER OVER THE *EDGE* ALL RIGHT... SHE KEPT COMING *BACK* FOR IT! SEEMED TO BE WHAT SHE *WANTED*... I COULDN'T *SEE* STRAIGHT. I DIDN'T KNOW WHAT *SHE* WANTED OR WHAT *I* WANTED OR WHAT WAS *RIGHT*.
I WAS THINKING *I* SHOULD TELL HER FUCKIN' *BROTHERS* ABOUT ALL THAT-- I JUST HADDA GET *OUT* OF THERE!

WHAT, THE ASCIANS DIDN'T HAVE ANY *NICE* GIRLS?

NOT THAT WOULD THROW THEMSELVES AWAY ON A SIN-EATER.

SO... I STARTED CHASING TOWN GIRLS, WHENEVER I COULD. IT FELT LIKE A WAY OUT OF THE CRAZY.

AND MOSTLY, IT **IS**... **THEY** DON'T KNOW SHIT ABOUT MY BEING A SIN-EATER.

I CAN JUST... NOT *TELL* THEM.

CAN'T DO THAT WITH ASCIANS.

THAT'S ONE LIE I COULD NEVER PULL OFF.

BACK IN THE DAY, I HAD THIS AUNTIE. OLDER THAN **HELL.**

EVERY TIME I GOT LAID, SHE KNEW.

ASCIAN GIRL, TOWN GIRL, HULDRE GIRL... NO MATTER HOW CAREFUL OR CAGEY I WAS, SHE *ALWAYS* KNEW.

AND *EVERY TIME* SHE DID THE *SAME* THING.

SHE'D LOOK ME UP AND DOWN.

THEN SHE'D LOOK ME IN THE EYE FOR A LONG MINUTE.

... *THEN* SHE'D SAY--

"IT'S NOT LOVE".

DROVE ME **BATS!** SHE'D NEVER **EXPLAIN**, SHE'D NEVER SAY **ANYTHING** MORE ABOUT IT!

AND IT'S NOT LIKE I COULD AFFORD TO HAVE ANY-BODY HEAR ME SCREAMING MY HEAD OFF ABOUT IT.

SO... ALL MY LIFE, WHENEVER SOME GIRL'S GOOD ENOUGH TO SLEEP WITH ME FOR THE FIRST TIME, I HAVE TO GET **AWAY** FROM HER IN THE MORNING. A WEEKEND'S REALLY PUSHING IT.

I NEED TO GO OFF BY MYSELF FOR A WHILE. SOMETIMES AN HOUR, SOMETIMES A WEEK, BUT I GOTTA DO IT. I'M **REALLY** AN UTTER PRICK IF I DON'T.

I HAVE TO... SEE IF MY MENTAL FURNITURE'S BEEN REARRANGED AT ALL, THINK OF MY AUNTIE, SEE WHAT SHE'D SAY.

SO... HAS SHE EVER? SAID, "IT'S LOVE"?

OH, SURE.

TH' BITCH.

WAS SHE RIGHT?

SHE'S **ALWAYS** RIGHT.

EXCUSE ME.

NINE HOURS AGO, I BROKE OFF THE SINGLE MOST POINTLESSLY AGONIZING ONE-WAY RELATIONSHIP OF MY YOUNG LIFE.

IT WAS A THIN SLICE OF HELL AND NOW IT IS **OVER**. HE'S NOT MINE. HE NEVER **WILL** BE MINE AND I'VE THROWN AWAY THREE YEARS OF MY LIFE PINING AND HOPING.

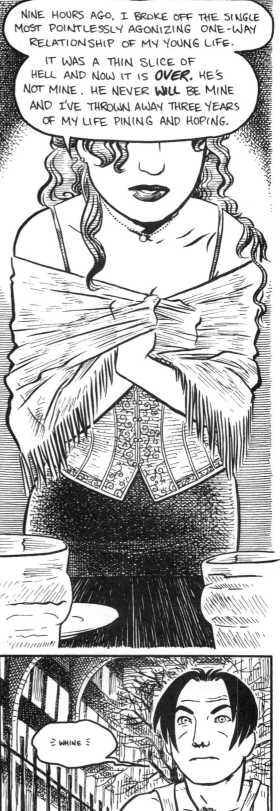

WELL, NOT ANYMORE, AND I NEED TO GET HIM OUT OF MY SYSTEM. I'VE GIVEN THE MATTER SERIOUS THOUGHT, AND ALL I WANT NOW IS FOR SOME TOTAL STRANGER TO NAIL ME TO A MATTRESS FOR THE NEXT FOURTEEN HOURS.

I WILL ALMOST CERTAINLY CRY ALL OVER YOU AND CALL YOU BY HIS NAME, BUT I ASSURE YOU THAT MY SEXUAL FRUSTRATION HAS BUILT TO SUCH A FEVER PEAK THAT I WILL FUCK YOU **DRY**.

WHAT DO YOU SAY?

≶ WHINE ≶

23

UHHMM...

I AM ...SO INCREDIBLY SORRY, MISS.

I AM ACTUALLY GAY.

...SORRY...

OH, NO NO, IT'S OKAY. REALLY. ≡SNIFF≡

I'M VERY FLATTERED, YOU UNDERSTAND...

-- BUT MY FRIEND HERE, HE'D BE GLAD TO -- OH, DAMMIT--

OWH

WUMP!

SHIT! OH THANKS, THANKS *TOO* MUCH. I DON'T HAVE ANY TURTLENECKS CLEAN.

TREASURE YOUR HICKEYS WHERE YOU FIND 'EM, PAL.

AND GET US ANOTHER ROUND.

HUT-

ASCIAN WOMEN ARE DIFFERENT. THEY'RE USED TO MORE *MOBILE* MEN.

≡HHAHA≡

A GUY CAN BE MARRIED TO *SIX* GIRLS IN *SIX* DIFFERENT CAMPS IF HE CAN GET 'EM. IT'S BAD FORM TO HAVE TWO WIVES IN THE *SAME* CAMP, 'LESS THEY'RE SISTERS, BUT APART FROM THAT, THEY DON'T MUCH CARE.

'N IF THEY *DO* GET THE REDASS AT YOU, GETTING *UN*MARRIED IS NO BIG THING --

YEAH, I THINK I SAW SOMETHIN' ON TV ABOUT THAT. ALL SHE HAS TO DO IS CHUCK YOUR SHOES OUT THE FRONT DOOR AND YOU'RE DIVORCED?

PRETTY MUCH.

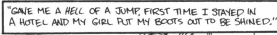

"GAVE ME A *HELL* OF A JUMP, FIRST TIME I STAYED IN A HOTEL AND MY GIRL PUT MY BOOTS OUT TO BE SHINED."

"*OH*, YEAH. I HAD A BOYFRIEND DUMP ME THAT WAY. FIRST HINT OF TROUBLE WAS, I GOT HOME AND ALL MY SHIT'S IN THE YARD."

SEE -- MY PEOPLE ARE NOMADS. NO *MAN* OWNS A HOUSE. THE TENTS ALL BELONG TO THE WOMEN. *THEY* DECIDE WHO GETS TO SLEEP UNDER THEIR ROOF.

BASIC'LY, IF SHE LETS YOU IN THE DOOR, SHE'S AT LEAST *CONSIDERED* SLEEPING WITH YOU.

≡HEH≡ ALL THE PARTS OF A TENT -- THE WORDS FOR THEM -- ARE IDIOMS FOR THE PARTS OF A WOMAN'S BODY.

É AMAL ALA'IWA.

HUH?

IT'S A SAYING. HANGS BY THE DOOR OF AN ASCIAN TENT. LIKE A "WELCOME" MAT.

MEANS "ENTER, FRIEND"!

...*LITERALLY* TRANSLATED.

--BUT JUST CAUSE SHE LETS YOU IN FOR ONE *NIGHT*, EVEN IF SHE HUMPS YOU TILL YOU **STEAM**, IT DON'T MEAN YOU'RE MARRIED! YOU'RE SUPPOSED TO CLEAR OUT AND WAIT FOR HER TO INVITE YOU BACK **IN**, NOT HANG AROUND WAITING TO GET **FED** LIKE A *STRAY DOG!*

WELL, NOT *HERE*. MOST A' THE WOMEN *I* KNOW, AND A SURPRISINGLY LARGE NUMBER OF MEN -- SEX IS LIKE **GLUE**. SLEEP WITH 'EM, AND BOND-O, YOU'RE IN A TRIAL MARRIAGE.

DISAPPEAR ON 'EM, AND YOU **ARE** A DOG.

DUMBASS WAY TO DO THINGS.

AS MAY BE--THEM'S THE **RULES**. YOU'RE FAR FROM DENSE, YOU *KNOW* THAT... YOU CAN'T PLAY BY **YOUR** RULES KNOWING THAT *THEY'RE* PLAYING BY DIFFERENT ONES AND EXPECT THEM NOT TO GET PISSED!

WHY EVEN WORRY ABOUT THE WAY ASCIANS DO THINGS, ANYWAY?

HOW MUCH OF IT EVEN APPLIES TO YOU?

WHAT **DOES** APPLY TO YOU SOUNDS LIKE A RAW

YOU MUST NEVER BE CRUEL TO A SIN-EATER, CHILDREN.

HE HAS ONE FOOT IN DEATH ALWAYS.

AND WHEN HE DIES, HIS SPARK GOES OUT. THERE IS NO SECOND LIFE FOR HIM. YOU'LL NEVER SEE HIM AGAIN.

BE KIND TO HIM IN THIS LIFE. YOU WON'T GET ANOTHER CHANCE.

IN EVERY LIFE...

EVERYBODY HAS TO CHOOSE...

THERE ARE CERTAIN RULES, IN MY LIFE...

YOU STAY AWAY FROM THOSE WHITE GIRLS. THEY'RE RAISED ALL WRONG. YOU *KNOW* IT'S NOTHING BUT TROUBLE.

STAY OFF OF THOSE WEIRDHEAD GIRLS, TOO.

I'M NOT KIDDING. STOP SMILING AT ME.

YOU'RE TOO **PRETTY** TO BE A SIN-EATER, THAT'S THE TROUBLE. IF ONLY HE'D ADOPTED YOU WHILE HE HAD THE CHANCE.

YOU'RE TO CUT THIS HAIR AND KEEP IT CUT. GIVEN THE HAIR ON YOUR **BODY** YOUR POOL OF WIDOWS AND ROUNDHEELS WILL SOON DRY UP.

BUT **YOU** STAY AWAY FROM THOSE WHITE GIRLS.

28

I WAITRESS HERE. MY NAME'S GRAZIE MAUGERI.

BUT YOU CAN CALL ME "THANK YOU".

I'M IN THE Ph.D PROGRAM FOR APPLIED PSYCHOLOGY AT TEMPLE UNIVERSITY. I'M WRITING MY DISSERTATION ON THE EROTICISM OF PITY.

...AND YOU'RE OFF NOW.

YEAH.

AND YOU WANT TO ...INTERVIEW ME.

OH YEAH.

OHH GOD. THANK YOU.

OOH. THAT'S RIGHT, BABY. YOU JUST KEEP ON SAYING THAT, I LIKE YOUR VOICE.

THERE'S NO JUSTICE IN THIS WORLD.

31

32

brief wake

NO, SERIOUSLY. SHE GREW UP IN A FUNERAL HOME. THE KIDS CALLED IT THE FUN HOME.

YOU THINK THAT WAS A ROAD-SIGN ABBREVIATION? I FIGURE--

SHE *DIDN'T* GROW UP IN A FUNERAL HOME. IT WAS THE FAMILY BUSINESS. YOU--

IS THE -- IS THE SIN-EATER HERE?

34

CHAPTER TWO:

SO!

JUST BACK IN TOWN, NO PLACE TO STAY, AS USUAL, HUH?

MAN, YOU'VE NEVER **SEEN** A PIECE' A WORK LIKE JAEGER!

TURNS UP OUTTA NOWHERE WITH *NOTHING* AND IN TWO DAYS HE'LL HAVE A ROOM AND A GIRLFRIEND!

HELL, SOMETIMES HE'LL EVEN HAVE A **JOB!**

HA HA

LET **US** DRAG YA HOME FIRST NIGHT, 'FORE YOU GET SERIOUS WITH SOME LADY SENATOR, OKAY? GET CAUGHT UP!

PLENTY OF ROOM, **RIGHT**, LIN?

SQUISH SQUISH ESS

CAN'T TELL ME YOU DON'T REMEMBER **THAT!** *I* WAS DRIN! TURNED ON THE FIRE HOSE AND THERE WAS NO WATER! AN! LITTLE GUY GOT TEN DAYS FOR KICKIN' A **COP!** HOW WAS I MEAN, COME **ON**-- ONE OF THOSE DAMNED PERFUMES T! OBABLY CALLED "MY SIN" OR "WHITE SHOULDERS" BUT **OUGHT** TO F___ CALLED "HARDER DEEPER" AND **THEN** SHE TURNS ___ A SISTER **THICE** AS HOT? ___ MARY, YOU KNO! ALL FELL OVER EACH ___ LIKE THE DO! ___ ARE, BUT WHO GOT ___? YOU, LIKE **ALWAYS DO!** NOT T. ___ GUY WHO'S YOUR ___ WIMMINS, YOU KNO! I ME

40

CLICK

RUSTLE

CREAK

HEY!

SEEYA.

NOW, I CAN'T SAY WITH ANY DEGREE OF *HONESTY* THAT I WOULDN'A LOVED TO WEAR THAT OUT LIKE IT AIN'T EVER BEEN WORE OUT BEFORE, BUT I KNEW *LINSEY* BEFORE SHE MET *VIC* AND THAT'S JUST WHAT SHE'S *LIKE.*

BAD *ENOUGH* WHEN MARRIED GIRLS DECIDE THEY AIN'T *THAT* MARRIED, BUT THIS WASN'T EVEN THAT. SHE WAS JUST PISSED AT VIC FOR WHAT-THE-FUCK-EVER.

I DON'T SO MUCH MIND BEIN' A SPARE *DICK* FOR THEM TO *AMUSE* THEMSELVES WITH, BUT DAMMIT I *HATE* BEIN' A HAMMER THEY HIT SOMEBODY *ELSE'S* NADS WITH.

41

Y'KNOW THEY ALL HAVE THEIR **MOMENTS.** SOMETIMES IT'S MORE LIKE MERE MOMENTS BEFORE **RABIES** SETS IN, BUT ME, I TRY TO TAKE THE **INCUBATION PERIOD** FOR WHAT IT IS.

TAKE LINSEY, FOR EXAMPLE; SWEET KID, MOSTLY.

SHE JUST WANTS SOMEBODY TO EAT HER COOKING AND TAKE HER DANCING AND SAY "POOR BABY HAVE A MARGARITA" WHEN SHE'S IN A SNIT WITH A GIRLFRIEND.

VIC'S THE OBLIVIOUS TYPE, SO WHEN SHE SULKS HE DOESN'T TRIP HER BREAKER.

HELL, IF IT WOULDN'T'A MEANT GOING TEN ROUNDS WITH **VIC** I'D'A DONE WHAT SHE WANTED. PROB'LY SHOULD HAVE. VIC'S NOT **THAT** TOUGH.

FIVE'LL GET YA TEN SHE TOLD 'IM I **DID** SLEEP WITH HER ANYWAY, AND THEY'RE FIGHTING FOR **REAL** NOW.

SO IF I'D **DONE** HER AND TAKEN A FEW LUMPS FROM **HIM** WOULD THEY BE FIGHTING OR UNITED AGAINST JAEGER THE DOUCHEBAG?

WHY IS IT WHEN YOU DO THE NICE-GUY THING, SEEMS LIKE **NOBODY** GETS ANYTHING THEY WANT?

WELL, RANDOM SEX, THAT'S ONE THING YOU NEVER KNOW WHAT YOU'VE GOT TILL YOU GET THE WRAPPER OFF OF IT.

WRAPPER.

KLUNK

SO YOU'VE MET CANDY TOO.

HUH?

SHIT, SHIT... I SWEAR SHE SEEMED COMPLETELY NORMAL. DIDN'T SET OFF THE PSYCHO-METER ONCE.

CUTE LITTLE GREEN-EYED BLONDE; I FREELY ADMIT I'M STUPID FOR GREEN EYES...

44

SO WHAT THE HELL, RIGHT? SHE'S A NICE SNUGGLY ARMFUL ALL THE WAY BACK TO HER PLACE.

EXACT CHANGE PLIZ!

BUT THEN SHE LETS US IN AND-- KA-**BAM**! SHE'S NOT INTERESTED ANYMORE.

LIKE AN ELECTRIC EYE ACROSS THE DOORFRAME WENT *CLICK* AND TURNED HER **OFF**!

I THOUGHT I'D BEEN UP-FRONT WITH HER -- I'D TOLD HER I NEEDED A **BED**, RIGHT?

SHE WAS OKAY WITH THAT-- SO I MUSTA LOOKED **GOOD** AND STUPID WHEN I REALIZED SHE MEANT ME TO SLEEP ON HER **COUCH**.

ALONE, THAT IS.

SO?

WHAT THE **HELL**. I'M **BEAT**. GET SOME **SLEEP**, MAKE HER **BREAKFAST** IF SHE'LL LET ME, GO MY **WAY**. NO HARM, NO FOUL.

BREAKFAST? UNGHH...

50

53

I CURLED UP IN HER BED AND WAITED LONG ENOUGH TO *DROOP.*

CAN'T NOBODY SAY I'M NOT *PATIENT--*

THE BED WAS TOO SOFT FOR MY BACK SO I GAVE UP AND HIT THE FLOOR.

I SLEPT HARD FOR ABOUT FOUR HOURS

--THAT'S A LOT FOR ME, I'M A CATNAPPER--

AND WHEN I GOT UP THERE WERE *THREE BIG THINGS.*

HER.

ASLEEP.

WEDGED BEHIND THE JAKES.

IN THE KITCHEN.

AN *ENTIRELY NEW CAKE.*

55

CHAPTER THREE:

OH NO, SHE'S EXACTLY THE TYPE I'D GO AFTER.

I MEAN THE WAY SHE WAS *BEFORE* SHE WENT ALL BATSHIT ON ME!

WELL *HELL*, NONE OF 'EM LOOK CRAZY WHEN I *MEET* THEM!

JUMPIN' JESUS ON A POGO STICK!

TALLY HO

SO YOU WENT TO A MEET-MARKET.

YOU HAVE FIVE MINUTES TO MAKE AN IMPRESSION AND WR... IN YOUR IMPRESSION DON'T ... FOUR YOUR HEART AND ... SOUL INTO IT JUST MAKE... A NOTE OF WHICH ONES Y... U'D LIKE TO TALK TO AGAIN ... JUST USE CHECKS AND ... EXES BUT DON'T BE O... STENTATIOUS WITH THE ... EXES THEY HATE T... AT HERE'S YOUR ... UMBER MOVE ON ... HEN THE HORN BLO... S LEAVE THE BON... DING FOR LAT... ER THAT'S WH... AT THIS IS F... ABC... OKAY.

OKAY.

WELL, AH... TWENTY-FIVE WOMEN IN TWO HOURS?

IT'S A CHALLENGE, GOTTA ADMIT, THAT NOT EVERYBODY CAN RISE TO MEET--

FIVE MINUTES TO MAKE AN IMPRESSION. AND NO ALCOHOL.

OKAY.

WHAT THE HELL, RI

HONK

OKAY, NOW-- HURRI-DATE!

62

WHAT IN THE *HELL* CAN *I* SAY ABOUT MYSELF?

HI, I'M SORT OF A HIRED KILLER, BUT I DON'T ACTUALLY *DO* IT ALL THAT MUCH, KILL PEOPLE THAT IS, MOSTLY GOOD HEALTHY IT'S JUST A ASS BEATING!

IT *IS* FOR MONEY, THOUGH!

HI, I DON'T HAVE A JOB OR A PLACE TO LIVE, BUT THE WAY *I* WAS RAISED, THAT'S REALLY NOT THAT BIG A DEAL!

HI, I'M NOT MARRIED AND I'M NOT GAY AND I'M NOT CARRYING ANY DISEASES OR AT LEAST IF I DO IT'S NOT APPARENTLY CONTAGIOUS!

"HI, HOW DESPERATE ARE *YOU*?"

HI, I'M GENIE, I, AH—

WHY **YES**, MISS, YOU **ARE** NEXT IN THE CONGA LINE BUT IT IS **MY** HUMBLE OPINION THAT YOU SHOULD **STOP RIGHT HERE** AND I'LL TELL YOU **WHY:** MY NAME IS JAEGER OR AT LEAST THAT'S WHAT I **GO** BY, 'CAUSE I'VE GOT THAT MAN-OF-MYSTERY THING ALL OVER **ANYBODY.** THESE AREN'T GYM-QUEEN MUSCLES, I GOT 'EM THE OLD-FASHIONED WAY, BY RUNNING FOR MY LIFE FROM BIG THINGS WITH BIG TEETH, 'CAUSE I'M WILD AND RUGGED AND OUTDOORSY. BUT I **DO** CLEAN UP NICE AND EAT WITH THE RIGHT FORK, DON'T FART AUDIBLY **AND** IF PRESSED **CAN** SPELL "HAIRY-KNUCKLED TROGLODYTE."

HEY, I'VE READ BOOKS AND SAT OUT IN THE RAIN WITH ABORIGINAL HOLY MEN AND HAD LIFE-CHANGING EXPERIENCES IN THE VERY **JAWS** OF **DEATH**--

I MAY NOT BE MARRIAGE MATERIAL, MISS, BUT EVERYBODY NEEDS A BAD BOY TO LOOK BACK ON AND **HEY,** I'VE GOT ALL MY TEETH AND I DON'T SMELL LIKE BEARING GREASE!

IF YOU WORRY ABOUT THE **MORAL** CONSEQUENCES OF CASUAL SEX, I CHARMED THIS COAT RIGHT OFF THE BACK OF A RHODOLITE PRIEST, AND YOU KNOW THEY'RE NOT EVEN **STRAIGHT** SO THERE'S THAT, I'VE GOT CONNECTIONS WITH THE MAN UPSTAIRS OR AT **LEAST** WITH HIS MEN **DOWNSTAIRS**--

ALL THIS PLUS A SIX-PACK **AND** I GET OUT OF YOUR HOUSE AT THE **FIRST** SIGN THAT YOU MIGHT BE GROWING **BORED** WITH ME, SO LOOK NO FURTHER, PRETTY THING, AND THAT'S **MY** HALF OF FIVE MINUTES RIGHT DOWN TO THE

HONK

≡ HEE HEE ≡

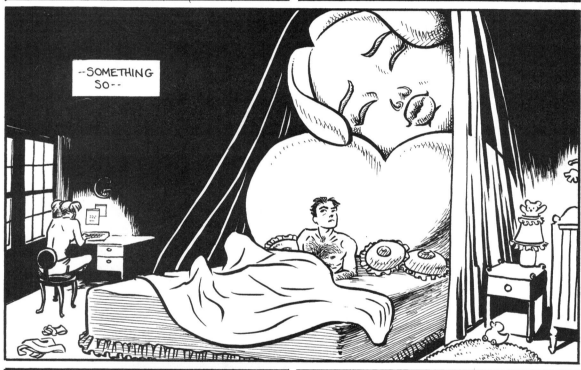

75

WE HAVE REALLY *DISTRACTING* SEX--

AND AS SO MANY TIMES BEFORE, I SCREWED IT UP BY FALLING **ASLEEP**.

MM... NO, ON SECOND THOUGHT WAKING UP WAS THE MISTAKE.

IF I HADNA WOKE UP I WOULDNA PASTED THE SHIT OUT OF HER

DADDY!

I'M REALLY NOT GOOD AT MORNINGS.

PWOOF!

SO, HERE I GO, DOWN THE STREET, LOTS OF TRAFFIC, FIRST-SHIFT COMMUTE, PEOPLE EVERY-WHICH-WAY AND AN OXYGEN MOLECULE CRYING BECAUSE IT'S ALL BY ITSELF.

IT'S NOT THAT HARD TO WIN A FIGHT. IT'S NOT THAT DIFFERENT FROM NOT GETTING INTO A CAR ACCIDENT. YOU JUST STAY IN THE SPACES WHERE NOBODY'S GOING TO HIT YOU.

SEEING WHERE THOSE SPACES **ARE** IS SOMETIMES EASY. IT'S A MATTER OF GETTING INTO THE CURRENT.

MOST PEOPLE DON'T *FIGHT*, THEY *DANCE*, THROWING PUNCHES ONE-TWO-**TURN**-ONE TWO-**KICK**.

SAME WITH TRAFFIC. IT'S EVEN **MORE** DISCIPLINED, THOUGH THE CHANCES YOU'LL GET **HIT** ARE GREATER BECAUSE OF THAT. SLOW DOWN, SPEED UP, TURN AT THE WRONG TIME, YOU GET OUT OF YOUR SAFE HOLE, AND KABOOMALA.

MOSTLY THAT **DOESN'T** HAPPEN. PEOPLE STAY IN THEIR PLACE AND WALK BLITHELY ON, HEAVY TRAFFIC BLASTING BY ALONGSIDE.

SO I SETTLED INTO THE JUMBLY RHYTHM OF THE WALKERS AND I HAD MY OWN SHIT TO THINK OVER BUT I DON'T LOSE TRACK OF THE FLOW THAT EASILY SO WHEN THIS GIRL TAPPED ME ON THE SHOULDER TO MACE ME IN THE FACE I JUST GOT OUT OF THE WAY.

ONLY **PROBLEM** WAS, THERE WAS ANOTHER GUY IN THE WAY THAT **I** VACATED AND SO **HE** GOT THE FULL BLAST, AND THIS WAS A REALLY **BIG GUY**--

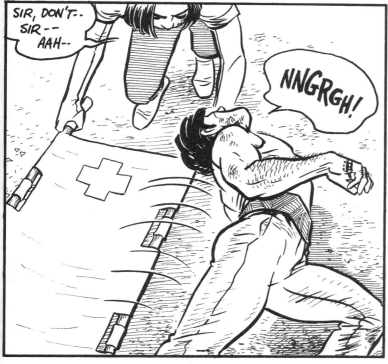

A PORNOGRAPHER WHO COSTUMES HIS MODELS IN BANDAGES, BETADINE, AND ARCANE MEDICAL EQUIPMENT.

WRAB PIRATE TV

PROSTITUTES WHO UNDERGO COSMETIC SURGERY TO RESEMBLE CELEBRITIES WHO DIED TRAGICALLY.

WRAB PIRATE TV

NURSES WHO HAVE SEX WITH THEIR PATIENTS!

WRAB PIRATE TV

SCHOOLGIRLS WHO LUST AFTER ABRASIVE, BAD-TEMPERED PROFESSORS!

≥HEH≤

DOES SEEING AN ATTRACTIVE PERSON MADE VULNERABLE BY ILLNESS OR INJURY PUSH YOUR GROWL-BUTTONS? DO YOU CRAVE TO LAY ON THE HEALING HAND? **WHERE** DO YOU CRAVE TO LAY IT?

WRAB PIRATE TV

COMFORTING THE SICK AS A SEXUAL FETISH! THIS IS THE MAJOR THEME OF MY WORK. I'M GRAZIE MAUGERI, RUMINATIVE JOURNALIST, WITH ANOTHER EPISODE OF

YOU SICK FUCK!

WRAB PIRATE TV

TODAY I'VE BEEN CALLED OUT TO OH HOLY HELL.

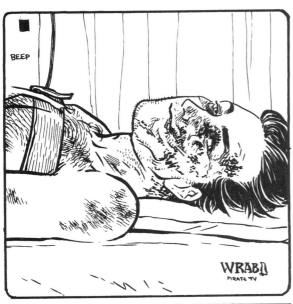

BEEP

WRAB
PIRATE TV

BEEP

OH, HELL, THESE HOSPITALS AND THEIR RF RESTRICTIONS. SIGNING OFF NOW--

CLICK

OH, BABY

OH, BABY-- THEY HAVEN'T EVEN CLEANED YOU UP YET--

IT'S NOT THAT BAD...

CHAPTER FOUR:

THE
TAIL
FAIRY

"SO."

" YOU WENT BACK TO GRAZIE, THE GIRL WITH THE MASTER'S THESIS AND THE FETISH TV SHOW."

NOW.

WHERE DOES IT HHURT?

"I WENT BACK TO GRAZIE, THE GIRL WITH THE FETISH."

"OH."

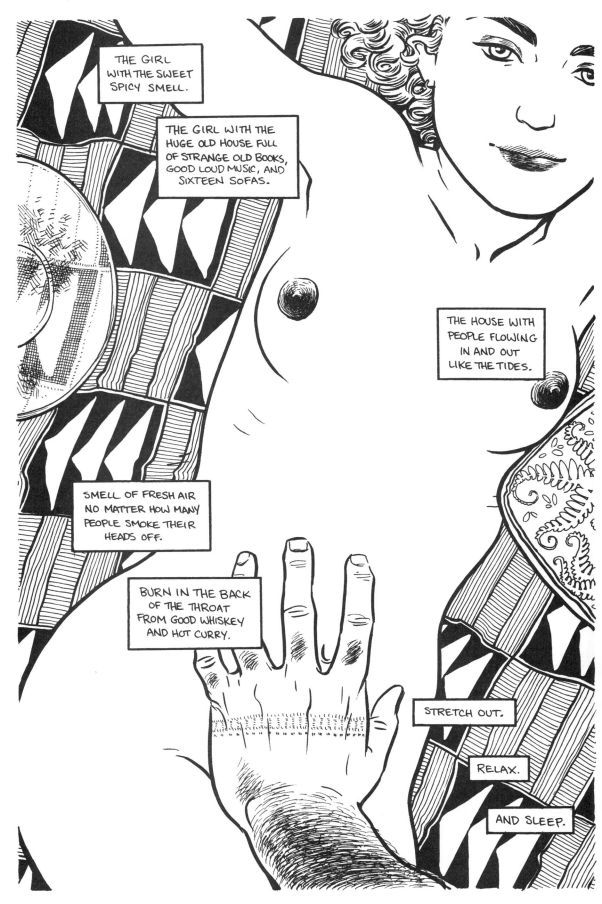

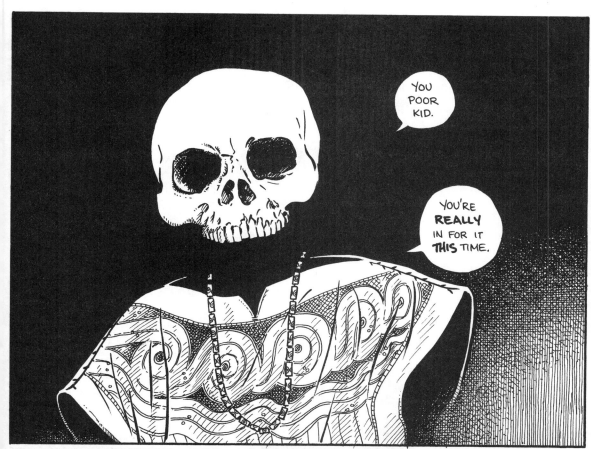

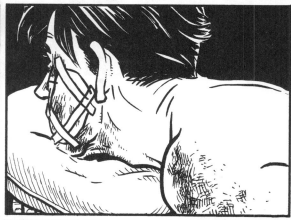

NOW WAIT A MINUTE.

WHAT?

YOU FELL OFF ONE OF THOSE GODDAMN DEATH-TRAP HIGH CURBS IN THE BUSINESS DISTRICT?

YEAH.

AND YOU *NATURALLY* GOT HIT BY A CAR AND WERE TAKEN TO A HOSPITAL?

I GOT *TAKEN* TO A *HOSPITAL* BECAUSE I GOT *HIT* BY AN **AMBULANCE**.

YOU GOT *HIT* BY AN **AMBULANCE**.

WELL *NO*, BUT THERE WAS ONE IN THE TRAFFIC FLOW AT THE SCENE. SO THEY STOPPED.

YOU'RE SAYING YOU WERE, WHAT, **KIDNAPPED** BY PARAMEDICS? FORCED INTO AN EMERGENCY ROOM AGAINST YOUR WILL?

HOW **ELSE** YOU THINK A TRIBAL LIKE **ME** IS GONNA GET HOSPITAL TREATMENT?

OH. THEY WERE HAVING A SLOW DAY, IS THAT IT? NOTHING BETTER TO DO?

IT'S LIKE I *TOLD* YOU--

AND **TOLD** ME, AND **TOLD** ME--

--IT WASN'T THAT BAD.

90

HAHA! DOWN IN FRAGGLE ROCK!

YOU'RE BETWEEN ME AND THE COFFEE.

I WANTED TO LOVE HIM.

AND THEN I DIDN'T.

AND THEN I WOULDN'T

AND THEN I COULDN'T

A CURIOUS RESERVE

HE ENGENDERS IT

IF THEY MOVE ME AGAIN

BURN DOWN THE BUILDING.

THAT'S JUST GAVIN.

HE LOOKS AFTER LIN'S KIDS, SORT OF INFORMALLY, GIVES HER A BREAK WHILE SHE'S HERE.

'COURSE THAT MEANS SHE'S HERE A LOT.

MARCIE?

HOW *ARE* YOU, BABY?

HOW'S —EVERY-BODY?

BRIGHAM EILUN GROSVENOR

BORN
DIED

MEMENTO

"SO CORRECT ME IF I'M *WRONG*—

95

HAVE YOU NOT ALWAYS SAID YOU HATE TO STAY MORE THAN THREE DAYS AT THE SAME HOUSE? TOO... APPALLINGLY DOMESTIC, I THINK IT WAS?

YEAH.

THERE WAS YOUR CHANCE; YOU SURELY COULD HAVE GONE TO THE SUMPTUOUS ABODE OF EMMA GROSVENOR AND CAUGHT UP WITH HER AND HER FAMILY, FOR ONCE WITHOUT HER HUSBAND IN THE WAY, AND YOU **DIDN'T.**

DIDN'T FEEL UP TO IT. PROBABLY SHOULDN'T HAVE GONE OUT AT ALL. HAD TO STOP A BUNCH OF TIMES ON THE WAY BACK.

YOU HUNG AROUND GRAZIE'S ALL THAT TIME.

YEAH.

BECAUSE YOU NEEDED TO CONVALESCE.

FROM "NOTHING MUCH" AND "IT'S NOT THAT BAD" AND "I DIDN'T GET HIT BY A CAR".

NEVER **SAID** I DIDN'T GET HIT BY A **CAR.**

NO, YOU JUST BLEW IT OFF LIKE IT WAS NOTHING.

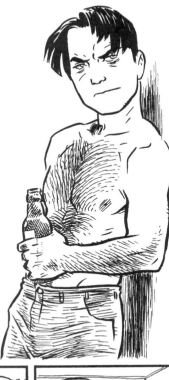

CRICK—

ANNG!

YOU OKAY?

YEAH.

YOU GOT A NEW TOOTH COMING IN?

BET YA GET A BIG QUARTER FOR THAT ONE.

THINK SO?

IF THERE'S *ANY* JUSTICE IN THIS OLD WORLD.

YOU'RE **SEXIST!** YOU KEEP SAYING **"HE"** LIKE IT'S ONLY **MEN!**

OUT OUT OUT FUCKING **OUT.**

I CHANGED MY MIND, EARL. EVERY BABY-RAPER I'VE EVER MET HAD TO BE A **HUGE** GODDAMN BULLSHIT ARTIST JUST TO **GET** AS FAR AS ADMITTING THEY'RE PEDOS.

"PRETTY STANDARD GRAZIE BEATDOWN. IF YOU CULTIVATE WEIRDOS SOMETIMES YOU HAVE TO **WEED.**

"HERE WAS THE PART THAT SURPRISED ME.

"GUY'S MAD. HE'S WALKING OUT. HE DIDN'T GET THE LAST WORD.

"HE HALF TURNED.

"AND THERE WAS SOMETHING IN THE WAY HE TURNED

"SOMETHING IN THE WAY HE WAS STANDING

A HOOK CAUGHT UNDER MY RIBCAGE

"HE TURNED AWAY AND THE CLENCH LET ME GO."

"I COULDN'T UNCROSS ONE OF MY EYES.

"IF HE *HAD* TURNED ONE FURTHER FRACTION OF AN INCH, IF HE *HAD* LOOKED AS IF HE MIGHT GO BACK INTO THE HOUSE, WOULD THAT MAN REALLY BE *DEAD* NOW?

"WOULD I BE SITTING IN JAIL AGAIN? DOPED UP HALF OUT OF MY MIND AGAIN?

"I'VE SEEN ALL KINDS OF FIGHTING.

"I'VE DONE ALL KINDS OF SHIT.

"BUT I DIDN'T KNOW I WAS LIKE *THAT*."

LIKE WHAT?

LIKE A MINE, READY TO BE STEPPED ON?

LIKE A DUMB SHIT THAT COULD THROW A BABY DOWN THE STAIRS. THAT COULD BREAK HIS GIRLFRIEND'S NECK AT BREAKFAST. THAT COULD SWERVE A CAR INTO A CONCRETE ABUTMENT FOR **NO** REASON. **NO** REASON AT ALL.

LIKE A DOOMED, BRAINLESS FUCKPIG.

CRAZY BITCH BUT CH...

FUC... SO GOOD

JUST BECAUSE ARRANGED MARRIAGES ARE THE RULE DOESN'T MEAN THERE ARE NO LOVE-MATCHES.

MY PARENTS BROKE AN ARRANGEMENT FOR **ME**.

AND I HAD A GOOD LIFE WITH HIM. BUT I COULD NEVER NEVER NEVER **EVER** BE UNHAPPY FOR ONE *INSTANT* WHERE ANYONE COULD SEE ME, AS LONG AS HE LIVED.

I THOUGHT PUTTING ON MOURNING CLOTHES WOULD BE A SORT OF RELIEF.

YOU CAN'T HAVE ANY OF THESE WOMEN.

YOU'VE GOT BLOOD ON YOUR HANDS.

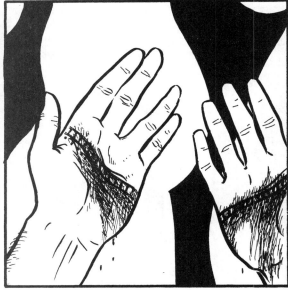

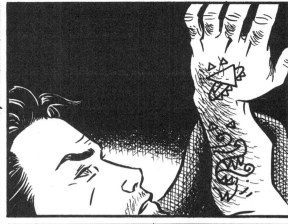

IT'S, WELL... I'VE HAD IT SINCE WE WERE KIDS. SINCE RIGHT BEFORE DAD DIED. DON'T KNOW IF YOU KNEW MUCH ABOUT THAT.

NOT MUCH. WE WERE ALL OUT OF SCHOOL BY THEN.

"I DID HEAR ABOUT YOUR HOUSE BURNING DOWN."

"YEAH."

"WELL ANYWAY, EVERY ONCE IN A WHILE, I GET THIS THING THAT SETS IN.

"IT'S MORE LIKE WHEN YOU TAKE IT *TOO* EASY, Y'KNOW? SLEEP FIFTEEN HOURS AND WAKE UP FEELING EVEN WORSE?"

AND YOU FEEL SO **BAD**, RIGHT, ALL YOU WANT TO DO IS **REST**, BUT STAYING DOWN IS THE *PROBLEM*, SO--

SO WHAT DO YOU DO?

USUALLY A BLEEDING FIXES IT RIGHT UP.

A **BLEEDING**.

YEAH.

AND YOU HADN'T DONE THIS BY THIS POINT BECAUSE ...?

POO--OO-HOOR--

BAY-AY-AABY--

EH...

JUST KEPT TELLING MYSELF I COULD PUT UP WITH THE LESSER SYMPTOMS IF THEY GOT HER HOT.

103

I'D BEEN WITH HER BEFORE, REMEMBER.

WASN'T LIKE *THAT,* I CAN TELL YA.

GRAZIE, SHE'S--

NEVAEH, *STOP.* JUST *STOP.* I KNOW YOU *MEAN* WELL, BUT--

--YOU'RE TALKING ABOUT *ONE* PERSON MOST OF US KNOW, AND ANOTHER THAT SOME OF US KNOW. TWO *PEOPLE.*

YOU ARE SPEAKING IN GROSS GENERALITIES WITH **NO** FACTS, WHICH IS HOW THIS WHOLE THING GOT BLOWN OUT OF PROPORTION IN THE FIRST PLACE. YOU--

BLOWN OUT OF **PROPORTION??** HE *STRUCK* HER, *THAT'S* A FACT! HE PUT HIS *HANDS* ON HER IN A *VIOLENT WAY!* IF IT WERE *ME* IN THAT SITUATION, I WOULD DO ANYTHING I *HAD TO* TO DEFEND MYSELF, AND I *STAND* BY THAT TO MY *DYING BREATH!*

NEVAEH, HE SMACKED HER ASS AT A COOKOUT.

YOU EVER BEEN IN THAT SITUATION?

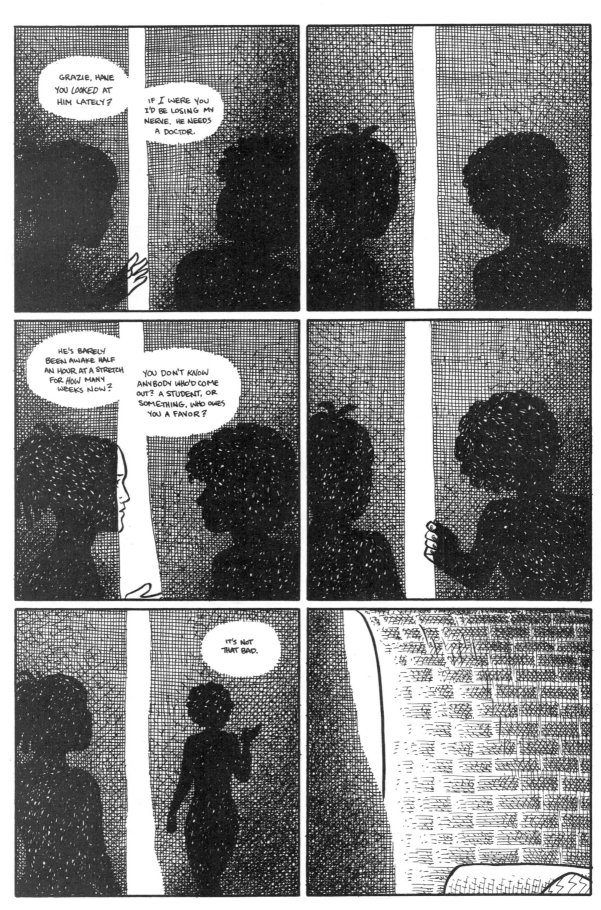

108

MOST PEOPLE DON'T BELIEVE IT, BECAUSE IT'S TOO HARD. KNOWING WE'RE ALL ONE WRONG STEP AWAY FROM DEATH, DISFIGUREMENT, PAIN FOR THE REST OF OUR LIVES.

EVERYBODY BUT **YOU.** I'VE **SEEN** IT, BECAUSE **I** WAS THE ONE WHO FUCKED YOU UP WITH THE CHAIR LEG AT PNEUMO'S THAT ONE NIGHT AND I **SAW** IT.

YOU GREW BACK TOGETHER LIKE NOTHING I'VE EVER SEEN WITHOUT SPECIAL EFFECTS. HERE I WAS READY TO BLAME MYSELF THE REST OF MY LIFE FOR WHAT I'D DONE TO YOU, AND YOU WERE **YOU** AGAIN BY MORNING.

A LITTLE SQUASHY IN SPOTS, MAYBE, AND BULLSHITTING AWAY LIKE NOTHING HAD HAPPENED, AND I JUMPED EVERY TIME YOU SO MUCH AS CLEARED YOUR **THROAT.**

FIGURED YOU'D GO **"BRAAAINS!"** ANY **MINUTE.**

WHY YOU BEAT ME WITH A CHAIR LEG, ANYWAY?

WE'RE GETTING OFF THE **SUBJECT** HERE, THE **SUBJECT**--

OH NO NO, I WANNA HEAR THIS. EIGHT **YEARS** I BEEN WISHING I'D CATCH UP WITH WHOEVER DEALT ME SUCH A STOMPING SO I COULD FIND OUT, WHAT DID I FUCKING **DO?**

I FORGET. MY **QUESTION** IS, YOU DON'T THINK YOUR CHRONIC ILLNESS HAS ANY RELATION TO YOUR SPECIAL EFFECT?

OW.

...WHAT'S THIS OILY BLACK SHIT?

ANCIENT TRIBAL REMEDY.

WHAT? YOU DIDN'T PUT THAT ON, IT CAME OUT WITH YOUR BLOOD--

WHY SHOULD IT?

GOTTA ADMIT...

I'VE NEVER LET MYSELF GET SO CLOSE TO IT.

TO WHAT?

POINT OF NO RETURN.

WHAT DO YOU **THINK** WOULD HAPPEN?

NO IDEA.

NOTHING GOOD.

BY THAT TIME
ALL I WANTED TO
DO WAS SLEEP.

AND SLEEP.

AND SLEEP.

I HAD LONG SINCE
STOPPED DREAMING.

I WAS
EMPTY.

GETTING
EMPTIER.

IF I DIDN'T
GET UP

I COULD
FEEL IT

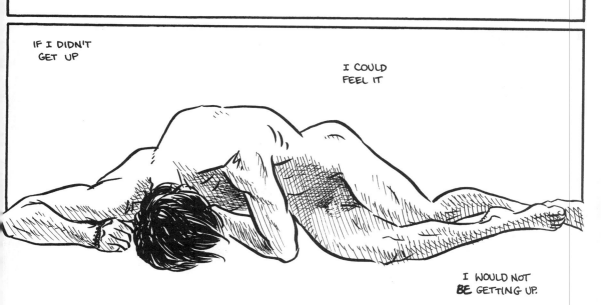

I WOULD NOT
BE GETTING UP.

"SEE, MY...
'SPECIAL
EFFECT'.

OKAY.

OKAY.

FIVE
MINUTE
BREAK.

OKAY,
TWO
MINUTE
BREAK.

UNH.

BETTER
MAKE THAT
A ONE MINUTE
BREAK.

"IT DOESN'T
FEEL VERY
GOOD.

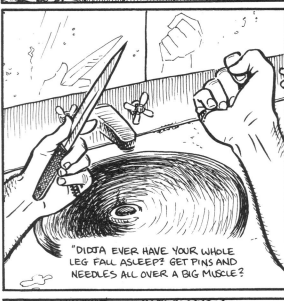

"DIDJA EVER HAVE YOUR WHOLE
LEG FALL ASLEEP? GET PINS AND
NEEDLES ALL OVER A BIG MUSCLE?

"DIDN'T IT MAKE YOU
WANT TO JUMP AND
FLAIL AND SCREAM
YOUR HEAD OFF?

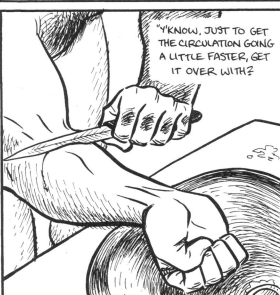

"Y'KNOW, JUST TO GET
THE CIRCULATION GOING
A LITTLE FASTER, GET
IT OVER WITH?

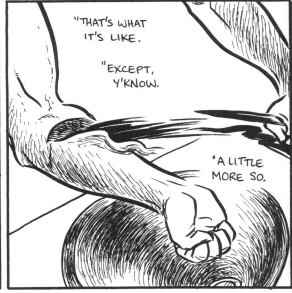

"THAT'S WHAT
IT'S LIKE.

"EXCEPT,
Y'KNOW.

"A LITTLE
MORE SO.

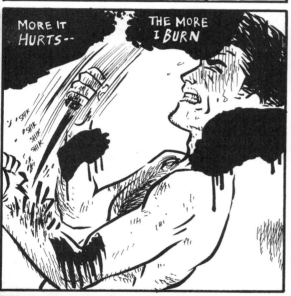

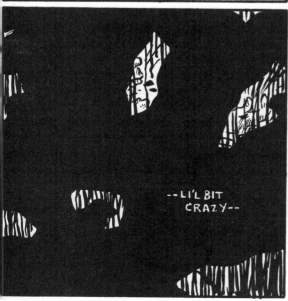

114

WE HAVE YOUR T.V. WE ARE PIRATE BROADCASTING. SIT STILL.

TIME FOR ANOTHER EDITION OF YOU! SICK! FUCK!

HEY, JAEGER?

FIVE
CRAZY
WOMEN

FINISHED JUNE 18 2006
CARLA SPEED McNEIL

NOTES

Chapter head image:
Inspired by George Platt Lynes' *Portrait of Reginald Beane,* 1938. Lynes was a brilliant composer of light and shadow, and a connoisseur of erotic male beauty. Pen-and-ink version of the cover used for *FINDER* issue #30, in which *BEWARE OF DOG* first appeared.

Page 6
Nothin' against Elvis Presley as such, but the original lyrics of *HOUND DOG* make more sense. The song was written for a woman, R&B singer Big Mama Thornton

The public phone he's using isn't connected to its base by a wire, but by a chain. The earpiece connects to the transmitter wirelessly. Only the desperately poor use these things, and no one expects privacy from the lowest of the low ends.

Page 7
Mattie is using the far more common information interface, one mounted into her skull behind the ear. The button only activates or deactivates the phone, the rest is all done by bone conduction of the voice.Yes, you can still roll over on your phone button and make a random phone call, like bumping your cell phone's redial button, if you forget to tell your phone to shut off.

Page 8
Having activated their skull-jack phones, holding their right hands in the 'phone' gesture keeps the call live. They don't have little receivers built into their hands; it's all brain.

There are 'day' neigborhoods in Anvard in which the sunlamps never shut off, and 'night neighborhoods where there are none to begin with. None of them are open to the sky. The most expensive property runs under the surface of the city's dome, which, though opaque, transmits several useful wavelengths of solar radiation, and is the closest thing to living in natural light available to city dwellers.

People are so cut off from the cycle of day and night that they hardly know what they are. Born a night person? Move to a dark town. Get depressed without enough sun? save up and move out. Just buy good blackout curtains and keep your sleep drugs handy.

A truly twenty-four hour city.

Simone's earrings are teeny tiny bars of soap-on-a-rope.

Page 9
The name 'Jannie' came from Shirley Jackson's elder daughter. The same woman who wrote The Haunting of Hill House and The Lottery also wrote funny home-life stories for ladies' magazines. The odd connections between events and details that ended up both in her humor pieces and her ghost stories are striking and occasionally unnerving. For a fuller appreciation of this amazing writer, go find Raising Demons and Life Among The Savages.

Jaeger really is a very good cook. Fancy cooking is a courtship ritual among the nomadic Ascians, who can rip out amazingly sophisticated food over dung fires. There's a big difference between 'Men's' cooking and women's, moreso even than the old 'women are cooks, men are chefs'. One of these days I'll get around to showing Jaeger talking some semi-urbanized Ascians into opening a restaurant.

Page 10

There's a radio speaker built into the cell tower that hosts this phone. Noisy, noisy town.

Page 11

Anvard is a city of towns stacked on top and halfway through each other. In some areas people live in pubs and smoke a lot. In others that kind of thing will get you forced into rehab for the good of your neighbors.

Page 12

The 'pub cat' here is a little bipedal dinosaur, as seen in panel three.

Vary of *Mystery Date* and her fellow artists and health specialists tend to use terms like 'monosexual.' Others people still use terms like 'gay' or 'straight,' limited though they may be.

Page 13

What has Jaeger got? What has his friend got? Those are all for later, later stories.

Pages 14-17

Ah, Frankie the Ho. He knows that most of the men he goes after won't be able to get it up while drunk enough not to kick his ass, but Frankie keeps hope alive. His wife, a practical woman, can't understand why he doesn't try some experimental brain reloads that would reroute his fetish for public sex into a fetish for getting the hell beat out of him. Whatever you do, she reasons, you should enjoy...

Page 18

This pub is in a night neighborhood. The streets are never much better lit than this. There is no sky, only the undersides of other buildings. In a richer neighborhood, those undersides would be fancier and better maintained, architecturally integrated into one another. Spaces between buildings would be wider and more open. The lower the income bracket an area enjoys, the twistier and narrower the streets are, until they're too small for any but foot traffic. There are families who have bought contiguous properties in all directions, until their sets of interconnected houses extend everywhichway like tunnels through a termite mound. Only there can people pool together enough money to break down a few walls and ceilings to make a garden room, a space to breathe, installing full- spectrum lamps and hiring gardeners to make little islands of green in the depths of the city.

Page 20

Huldres are farmers. They live in giant combine harvesters, rolling around the hills outside the cities, mowing the grain which, according to them, grows wild. Other harvesters take issue with their methods. Huldres are pirate farmers.

Page 21

This is one of my many attempts to dig myself out of the crosshatching trenches: colored pencil on linen-finish paper. Only problem is, I have to do the word balloons on stick-down labels. Letter, cut out, stick down. Tedious work, and it limits what you want to do with balloon shapes, numbers of balloons per panel, and other tricks of the trade.

Page 22

Some people have to know they're in love before they have sex. They have to see if their mental furniture has been rearranged before they want to get physical. Jaeger's just the opposite; his mental furniture doesn't really get rearranged unless he has sex with someone.

Page 23

No, this is not me. Huh, don't I wish.

Page 25

I've never really been happy with this guy's design. He looks all Village People with the mustache, and just such a nonentity without it. Ah well, years to go and many miles to cross; he'll come into his own in time.

Page 26

Damn, the perspective on panel three is wonky. I know how I did it, too; it was correct on the pencilled panel, but I moved Jaeger down to fit more of the ceiling in. So his boots, in the foreground, look big enough for him to get both legs in one. Oops.

This notion of architecture being related to the female body I got from traditional Russian architecture. Those characteristic onion domes, apart from being great at shedding heavy snow, reflect the shape of the old woman's headdrss, the tiara-like kokoshnik. Or kokoshniks reflect the shape of onion domes. Dunno which, it's probably a little of both.

Page 28

The 'weirdhead' girls are people like the Huldres, who have horns and cows' ears, and the lionlike Nyima-- humanoid people with animal characteristics.

Ascians are repulsed by body hair. They don't have much, and what they do have, they shave. Jaeger's hairiness really sets him apart from them.

Page 30

'Maugeri' is Sicilian in origin. 'Grazie' is of course an Italian word, but as far as I know it isn't an Italian name.

So it's just her.

Page 31

I did a short follow-up story between Jaeger and Grazie for an erotic anthology called *Smut Peddler*. It isn't in this collection because, though it was fun, it really didn't advance the story. There aren't any big song-and-dance numbers in Finder, either.

I've done three short smut pieces as of the date of this writing. I'll probably do more. Perhaps someday I'll have enough to print the *Finder* pillow book.

Page 32

Jaeger and his friend both come from the same company town. They were kids together.

The friend's name is Brom, okay? There. Brom is singing Devo. Devo is good.

INTERLUDE: BRIEF WAKE

Page 33

This is also a night neighborhood. The blonde in the second panel has only three fingers on each hand. She is a construct. That's all for later too.

Page 34

'Chane' rhymes with 'Jane.' These are Ascians in the uneasy process of assimilation.

Page 35

This all has to do with the near-universal state of war that exists between roving bands of Ascians. Women do have to move from band to band to find a husband, and they do it in a variety of ways-- some captured, some traded, some volunteer. They go seeking husbands from men who may have killed their brothers and fathers, and who may yet kill their blood kin. Lots of bad blood. But the kids have to be accepted, and this ritual is all about assimilation. All the hate and despair and vengefulness is supposed to be dumped on the sin-eater.

Pages 36-37

The sin-eater's ritual as it was practised in Appalachia had to do with the dead, and the mourners at the wake. The corpse was covered by its shroud, and food laid out on top of it. The sin-eater could either come and eat only that which he could cram down in one sitting, or else had to stay until he had consumed all the food. In Britain the rituals used salt and bread, sometimes wine, and the sin-eater had to go straight to th nearest water to be purified. Ancient Jewish sin-eaters were animals, 'scape-goats, which had prayer scrolls tied around their necks and into their coats, and which were then driven away to fend for themselves in the wilderness.

Ascian sin-eaters perform a wide variety of rituals, up to and including executioner. In that capacity, the sin-eater uses a hammer.

CHAPTER TWO: SO

This chapter first appeared as issue #38 of *FINDER*, and was the last one sold as a single issue. The issues weren't losing money, but they weren't making much either, and sales on the issues had been stagnant for over a year. If the issues were meant to be advertising, then they weren't doing their job.

So the book went on-line after that. There have been plenty of kinks to work out, but in the long run this will be better. Chapters can be as long or as short as I want them to be, and, though the deadline for producing this graphic novel has made me bleed from the eyes, working straight through has been strangely satisfying.

Of course, so is Rapture of the Deep, or so I'm told.

I also wrote and pencilled a seventeen-page story that was meant to serve as a bridge between BEWARE OF DOG and this first part of FIVE CRAZY WOMEN that I had to cut for lack of time. It's done, it's just not inked. I'll do something with it eventually. I just simply could not have got it inked and still come out with the book on time. I slapped BRIEF WAKE together to take its place.

Why did I need the interlude story in the first place? BEWARE OF DOG was issue #30. FIVE CRAZY WOMEN began in issue #38. A lot of time and a whole other story, THE RESCUERS, happened in between. BEWARE OF DOG was done as a stand-alone story, and that's fine, but it went a long time uncollected. I picked up its threads to do FCW, but I needed something to give the impression of time's passage. Not sure how well it worked. The longer story would have done that more effectively.

Jim Ottaviani said it best: "It's amazing how the front and back covers of a new book are exactly like a rock and a hard place."

Page 42
The line I cut from this page went "They never show me the crazy till it's too late to run away." Funny, but in retrospect it seemed to put a stop to the story's momentum.

Boy, it's just crazy to have the freedom to do things like that; when i was doing the issues it felt like a live performance. Couldn't go back and change things for the TPB. That's cheating.

Page 44
I had this daft idea that people wouldn't know who Jaeger was talking to if I just kept his face out of the way. It's so hard to get Jaeger to talk that it was important to keep his friend in the background as much as possible.

At this point Jaeger and his friend are sitting in a country store, long after hours. This kind of shop is found in dark neighborhoods, and serves a lot of purposes. This one sells whatever it can, and maintains an unofficial post office for people who can't send mail electronically.

'After hours.' That means 'closed.' The shop was closed but the doors weren't locked, so they went in.

Page 45
Candy's actual name is in fact Candle. Her mother was a pop musician, and got caught up in yet another wave of strange baby names.

The sandals she's wearing have no straps. They're just soles that adhere to your feet. Every once in a while a company will offer things like that, and they're always kind of intriguing as concepts and horrible in practice, so it was perfect for this character.

Page 46
Flirt flirt flirt and then look surprised when someone wants to go to bed with her. How many girls have I known who did this?

Oh yes, and Candy's front door lock is coin-operated. Yes, this is a really cheap neighborhood. It wants her thumbprint too, so it's not like anyone with a dime can get into her apartment.

Page 47
I really must get Jaeger out onto the plains one o' these days. Did I ever tell you about the time a group of Huldres sold him into slavery? No?

Pages 48-53
Food compulsions can be very strange. The uneaten cake is an obvious thing; she won't eat it but she has to have it in the house. The way she hides candy wrappers is a less obvious thing. She can't eat certain things in front of other people, and even in the privacy of her own home, she automatically hides the evidence-- even though, after a few hundred wrappers, they aren't hidden at all.

She lives on sugar. Lots of eating-disordered women do. It's widely considered 'safe' because it does not contain fat. Candy is obsessed with sugar. She dabs sweet extracts like vanilla and peppermint behind her ears in lieu of perfume.

Page 54
Not all women with eating disorders shy away from sex. Far from it. But this pull close/push away thing worked for Candy as a character.

Lucky for Jaeger; if he'd had sex with her, her part of this story would have been a lot longer and a lot uglier.

Page 55

Jaeger really is more comfortable on the floor. This has driven many a townie girlfriend half nuts.

Where did the new cake come from, if Candy's kitchen is completely empty except for the box of candy hidden under the sink?

CHAPTER THREE: TALLY HO

I chose that chapter title at the last minute. It captured the charging-in-chin-up-stout-fellow quality I wanted.

Well, and some more male-bonding snort-snort stuff. Tally them hos, boys. Make a list.

Page 59

Outside of town, Jaeger is a scavenger and a freelance fighter. In town, well, he's a scavenger and a freelance fighter. The rules change a bit and he loses track sometimes.

Page 60

There's a restaurant in San Diego called Buca Di Beppo. Its walls are covered in odd photographs; the women's bathroom is decorated entirely in fiftues foundation garments and hygiene pamphlets-- Lysol, anyone? The men's is full of phalli and images of Vesuvius. Ask for the Pope room if you don't have a really large group.

One of my favorite images is one of two young priests lighting cigars, remarkably like the image in panel four.

So this young priest catches Jaeger shaving in the holy-water font. I could not write the dialogue in this scene.

Page 61

I have no words to describe speed dating.

Page 62

I have no idea who any of these women are. I was just braindrooling. This page was done mostly to the soundtrack of The Crying Game.

Page 62

This is the first page I drew after having my second kid. Everything after this page was done between early March of '06 and mid-June. Don't go thinking "Hey, that's three months. That's not so bad." Hahahaha.

No, there's an agonizingly slow spin-up period after I've been out of it for a while, not to mention all I had was an outline, no script.

Production of the story issue by issue has been a treadmill I find myself very happy to climb off of. I took the time to write a full script for the rest of the book, and as a result I had time to edit.

Page 64

Inspired by Penn Jillette's rocketmouth spiel for Teller as seen on their show.

Page 65

Laaaa... and here's Genie. What can I say? She'll be back, if only in the Anvardian equivalent of the Darwin Awards.

Pages 66-68

Gymnastics. Yes. Limber little thing. Impulse control? No.

Page 69 haha

I'd originally palnned to have Genie's little nudie pic in heavy shadow, but it turned out too cute to obscure. The heavy-shodow version just looked strange, what with those silly pigtails bobbing around in the dark.

Page 70

She made that headboard herself.

She's very good with her hands.

Page 71

Ta-DAA. My sounding boards all told me to leave the poopin' part out. Genie's name, for those of you who don't have small kids, is a pun on a ghastly piece of modern baby equipment, the Diaper Genie. This is a trash can. Just a trash can. But it has an extra-long can liner that attaches to the lid. You dump a smelly diaper in through the hatch in the lid. You spin the lid. Smelly diaper is now encased in a twist of plastic garbage-can liner. Repeat until liner is full. Extract horrible turd link sausage and discard.

There is a cute smiling happy baby on the box. Really. Lots of parents have these things. Genie's relatively uncommon fetish pales in comparison with the prevalence of the Horrible Turd Link Sausage. Someday long after the asteroid hits and the radioactive cockroaches are excavating our landfills, the Turd Link Sausage will lend its name to our era.

My kids' diapers have cartoon characters printed on them. Winnie the Poo.

Page 72
Most of the Crazy Women have potential in future stories. I tend to think of established characters as Face Cards. People who've read previous books will recognize them, they carry a certain amount of weight. The Crazy Five may be more like the seven of diamonds rather than queens or aces, but they might have their uses... but I don't know about Germaine. Maybe that's why Jaeger doesn't count her.

Page 73
I got more letters after having posted this page, with its 'mutate' line, than I had received in years. Interesting.

Page 74
Don't ask me if Yekat counts or doesn't I was writing a character in a haze of sleep starvation while actually in a state of sleep starvation myself. I think she counts. Why she's still a nice girl probably has to do with the fact that she still lives at home.

Her name is a variation on Catherine, of which there are hundreds. Popular saint.

Page 75
Several beds pushed together, with their legs held together with rope. You can still lose your keys, your glasses, and your viagra down the cracks between mattresses, and have to send one of the kids under the bed to retrieve them.

Page 76
Well, I tried to indicate that the grandma was sort of bouncing around as the bed jiggled, but I'm not sure it came across.

Page 79
I definitely abbreviated that guy's bulk by turning his shoulder too far toward the viewer.

Page 81
He really got off pretty light.

Page 82
Here I'm depicting a reasonably advanced society, but they don't have collapsing gurneys for their ambulances. Yikes.

The medics are wearing full-body protective suits. Not much as armor goes, but they do protect them from a dull puncture like human teeth, from needle contamination, from splashing body fluids. They still need masks if things are really bad, of course.

And no, they should not be forcing down the head of a trauma victim in order to restrain him. But he's a pain in the ass when he's hurt.

One good thing about having small boys in the house: you've always got toy cars to use as models for street scenes.

Page 83
WRAB Pirate Television was a comic by the inimitable Matt Howarth, also creator of *Kief Llama, Savage Henry,* and *Those Annoying Post Brothers.* If all the world had one ass, his boots would still be big enough to kick it.

Hey look, it's Vary. Hi, Vary. Vary was the star of my sixth book, *Mystery Date.*

By the time I drew this page, I'd been done with Grazie for three years. It was good to see her again.

Page 84
Grazie has two floating cameras, one keyed to stay on her face, one keyed to whatever she's looking at. She can jump transmission from one camera to the other with an eyeblink signal.

She still works at the pub; pirate TV doesn't necessarily pay.

I was watching the first season of House MD while I was drawing this part. All the women seemed to have a phase of wearing low-cut frilly blouses under vests. Sort of... vulvar, if you ask me, but pretty.

CHAPTER FOUR: THE TAIL FAIRY

Page 86
The house is made of brick, built the old-fashioned way, not a single layer of brick over a balloon stickframe, but actually three layers of brick deep. The stairs are so old, there's a dip worn into each tread. This house has been in the family for a long time.

The large portrait on the left is of Grazie as a girl. These portraits are generally made as gifts for the family when a child wins full membership into her clan. Grazie's portrait should be hanging in her family's gallery. She stole it, along with most of the framed pictures she has on her walls. Long story.

The girl on the far left has one blue eye and one brown, and has bleached the hair on the blue-eye side and dyed the hair on the brown-eye side. She and the Huldre in the center (girl with horns) are the only ones who look a little odd, but nearly every person in Grazie's house is someone she's interviewed.

No, she has not had sex with all of them.

Page 88
If I'd had brain cells to spare, I could have made better designs for Grazie's couch collection. She loves couches. Everything happens on couches.

Page 89
That looks like a skull on the bookshelf, but it is actually a carnival mask.

Page 90
The roads in that part of the business district are laid in old subway pits, so the curbs are a good three feet high. It's easy to fall in. especially during high foot-traffic times. Nobody likes it, but nobody wants to fix it.

The thing is not that Jaeger is lying to his friend, but that he's doing it so badly. With his big issues, the closest he can get to honesty is a very transparent lie. His friend knows this part of him very well.

Page 91
He doesn't heal instantly. His bones, for instance, stay soft for a good long time, and it would be easy to kill him when he's in this healing state.

Page 92
Grazie has a fascination with all kinds of sexual fetishes, but hurt/comfort is all hers. She once considered becoming a counselor, but realized she'd have to be nice to people she thinks need a good slap upside the head. So instead she does her little TV show and has an ever-flowing stream of oddballs in and out of her house.

Page 93
Fever. I had the highest fever of my life back in February this year ('06). I really needed to get to the bathroom, and I just plain could not get up. I just huddled under the blankets shivering and waiting for it to subside, and it wasn't.

Kind of interesting, actually.

Page 94
Panel two: there's Genie. Panel three: there's Linsey. Panel six: Gavin is the squirrelly guy from the speed-dating event.

The dialogue between Lin and Grazie comes from a dream sequence in Cerebus: Church and State, part one, which was the first graphic novel I ever bought. The sequence was called 'Odd Transformations II' (the part of the dream that takes place after Cerebus gets up and pees for nearly four pages).

Dream sequences are generally used to jumble all the elements of the ongoing story together to reflect a turbulent moment in the plot, and the dreams in Cerebus are no exception, but other things seemed to be going on in them. This is part of a conversation between Astoria and the Countess, or at best Cerebus' mental images of them. Cerebus walks past them as if they aren't there, and their words hang in the air as if heard through a thin wall. I didn't refer back to the book to copy the exchange exactly, but rather used what I could remember.

Jaeger is rambling through Grazie's house like a ghost, sleeping in her living room, waking at odd hours and for short times, and these few lines from Cerebus have been stuck in my head for a long time. They seemed to serve the atmosphere of the page.

And there's Marcie. Hi, Marcie. Down, boys.

Page 95
For those of you who haven't read my first book, *Sin-Eater*, Brigham Grosvenor was Jaeger's officer while he was a military man. These women are his wife Emma and his kids, Marcie, Rachel, and Lynne.

Page 96
That T-shirt is, of course, quite pink. He's just wearing whatever Grazie's got in her grab bag.

Page 97
As Grazie would say it, "There are a lot of kinks out there. Most of 'em, maybe they don't do much for me, but I can at least see how someone could be turned on by 'em. I had a wild time with a guy in a mole suit once. Once, dammit, don't look at me like that! Other fetishes... ho boy. Some of 'em I just cannot see. Not even with a microscope.

"Kinky's all right with me. Just no liars, no whiners, and no users."

Pages 98-99
This bit came from a very ordinary-sounding guy who called in to a radio interview of a doctor specializing in post-traumatic stress syndrome. He said he was in Viet Nam, sure, but in spite of that never thought he had any real psychological fallout from his experiences there. He described this scene, standing outside the door of a party, truculent guest being asked to leave, and his own sudden realization that he could have-- would have-- killed that man if he'd really tried to go back into the house.
This guy was not a drifter, not homeless, not one of the lost. He thought he was just an ordinary guy, and he was stunned at this mechanical compulsion to kill. He'd never had it in civilian life. It really opened his eyes, he said, to what PTSD can really do.

It might just be one of those strange floating impulses that jit us all from time to time. Alan Moore described looking down at the top of his mother's head as she tied his shoes-- he was very young-- and thinking of taking a knife off the nearby table and killing her. Why? No reason. he wasn't angry with her. He wasn't abused. And for him there was no compulsion to act, and he wasn't even fully aware of the thought until later in his life-- though he didn't forget the incident.

There's a lot of weird stuff in our heads. Jaeger was briefly caught in a compulsion that could have triggered him to act. Could have. Might have. Didn't. So now he doesn't know.

There are no plants growing in Grazie's front garden. Those are all fake. She has some potted herbs under the lamps in the kitchen.

And there's Yekat. Song lyrics are from Buck Cherry.

Page 100
Baby Broken Bones appears courtesy of Scott Roberts, creator of *Patty-Cake and Friends*. He really has a handle on little kids. He does the occasional fake ad, and Baby Broken Bones was one.

It's not so far-fetched. When I was very young there was a baby-doll that got diaper rash that you could 'cure.' It was taken off the market because you gave it the diaper rash by putting a pill into the doll's bottle. Dolls supposedly model behavior, let's not forget...

And here's Candy. Why are all these randomly met girls in Grazie's house? And why doesn't Jaeger ask this question? Well, Grazie knows Linsey. The rest, well-- think of Grazie's house as like a well-attended message board. People you'd never expect drift in all the time.

And here's Germaine. Hi, Germaine. Bye Germaine. At certain angles she does resemble Jaeger's dad's last girlfriend very closely.

Page 101
Jaeger's aunt never had this conversation with him. She wasn't much for storytelling.

Page 103
"Yeah, what's a little hematoemesis among friends?" Just keep putting it off, you can take it...

Page 104

'Nevaeh' is 'Heaven' spelled backwards.

Page 106

In a very real way, Grazie's house is a website. For many people, the virtual environment is far more useful and desirable than the real one. Some physical locations are designed to bridge the gap. Cameras transmit images of the rooms to the web; and holostages make the visitors visible to the real world. Some people create simple digital puppets to go visiting with, avatars that pretty closely resemble themselves -- though few can resist the urge to tinker. Others bust out with role-playing game characters, or knockoffs of actors and celebrities. Not many houses have such large holostages, that was just Grazie's uncle's big thing.

Page 109

We're so used to characters in fiction never really getting hurt, their accidents and injuries having very few physical consequences. I resisted mightily the urge to include in this storyline more details on the genetic plagues that have swept various cities, including Anvard, in recent times. But, considering that these plagues can do things like make people fuse together like conjoined twins, I thought better of it... this was originally supposed to be a nice fluffy comedy.

Jaeger does have his quick-heal. But it isn't magic and it does have its backwash.

Page 112

The other reason he put off doing this for so long is that Grazie really hates cutters. She'd recently had a run on them in her house, and had to work hard to get them to stop hanging around. Of course, he cuts for a different reason, but, well. Keep reading.

Page 115

Pirate TV broadcasters can turn your TV on when you don't want it on. They control the vertical.

Page 118

Yes, well, these are two guys who've known each other a long time. there's a difference between a gaybashing and two friends smack-talking.

FRONT AND BACK COVERS

Well, the only one of the women on the front who has appeared before is Xini, the Ascian girl in the yellow tutu. The girls in the Crazy Bouquet are Marcie, Chane, Auntie, Rachel, Grazie, Candy, Yekat, Genie, Linsey, and Germaine.

And that's that. The next book will revisit the oldest Grosvenor sister, Rachel, and is titled *Voice*. It will run on-line at

www.lightspeedpress.com

and will be collected July '07 in advance of the convention season.

"Good night, and good luck."
                              --Edward R. Murrow

next in FINDER: